Louis Moyse Flute Collection

Moyse Collection of Easy Flute Classics

WITH A COMPANION CD

Recorded by Caen Thomason-Redus, flute
and Jeannie Yu, piano

ISBN: 978-1-4234-8279-6

G. SCHIRMER, Inc.

DISTRIBUTED BY

HAL•LEONARD®
CORPORATION
7777 W. BLUEMOUND RD. P.O. BOX 13819 MILWAUKEE, WI 53213

www.schirmer.com
www.halleonard.com

CONTENTS

LOUIS MOYSE (1912-2007)

The leading flute teacher of the twentieth century, Louis Moyse (pronounced mo-EEZ) was born in the Netherlands in 1912 while his parents were on a European tour. His father, Marcel Moyse, was a renowned French flute player that toured extensively world-wide, gave master classes, taught privately, and wrote several method books on flute playing. Louis learned to play the flute and piano expertly from his father, and chose to focus on the flute by the time of his acceptance into the Paris Conservatory. In 1932, he won the Premier Prix at the conservatory and began assisting his father, who was on the faculty.

In the late 1930s, Moyse was appointed second chair flute of the Boston Symphony. Before he could make the journey from France, the outbreak of World War II caused borders to close. Moyse was not able to take the position and spent the next few years in France performing on piano with his wife and father in the Moyse Trio. The group left France following the war and journeyed to the United States after some time in South America.

In the United States, the trio settled in Vermont and began teaching at Marlboro College. Joined by European friends Rudolf Serkin, Adolf Busch, and Hermann Busch, the sextet founded the Marlboro Music School and Festival. They envisioned a summer series of workshops without an instructor or coach. Instead, seasoned musicians play alongside less experienced musicians and pass along valuable tips through making music together. Moyse remained involved in this organization for many years, performing with and encouraging thousands of young musicians. He and his first wife, in the early 1950s formed the Brattleboro Music Center, now called the New England Bach Festival.

For the next several decades, Moyse taught at Boston University and the University of Toronto, and coached hundreds of students at the Marlboro Music Festival, and in master classes. From his Vermont home, Moyse instructed scores of students privately, composed and arranged nearly two hundred works, coached ensembles, led master classes, and edited many volumes of flute literature. The significance of his contribution to flute pedagogy in the twentieth century cannot be overstated. His editions have become the staple of nearly every flute studio and have come to define what is considered appropriate repertoire for the instrument. His master classes and ensemble coaching sessions were much coveted events attended regularly by students from around the world. Many of his private students are distinguished touring musicians and hold positions in the foremost orchestras. Moyse died at the age of 94 in 2007 of heart failure.

Musette
from English Suite No. 3 in G minor, BWV 808

Transcribed by Louis Moyse

Johann Sebastian Bach
(1685–1750)

Scotch Dance
Ecossaise in G Major, WoO 23 *

Transcribed by Louis Moyse

Ludwig van Beethoven
(1770–1827)

* Originally composed in G Major, Louis Moyse has transposed this ecossaise to C Major for easier performance on the flute.

Theme
from Six Variations on the Duet "Nel cor più non mi sento"
from *La molinara*, WoO 70

Transcribed by Louis Moyse

Ludwig van Beethoven
(1770–1827)

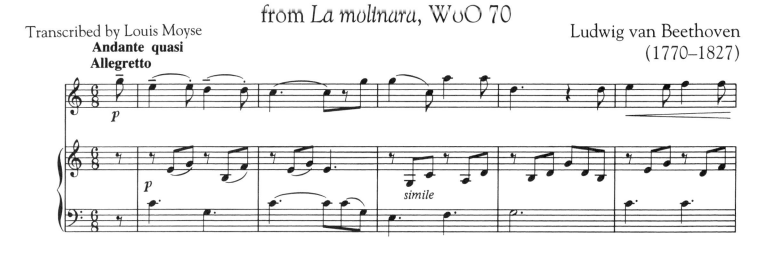

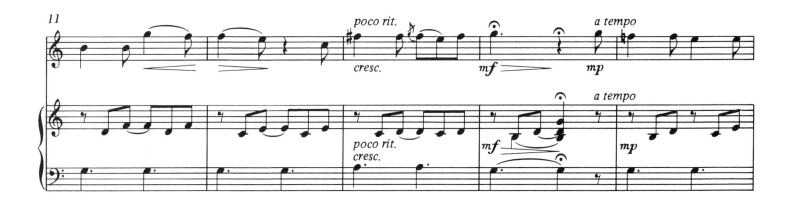

Waltz
from Sixteen Waltzes, Op. 39

Transcribed by Louis Moyse

Johannes Brahms
(1833–1897)

Prelude in A Major *
from Twenty-four Preludes, Op. 28, No. 7

Transcribed by Louis Moyse

Frédéric Chopin
(1810–1849)

* Originally composed in A Major, Louis Moyse has transposed
this prelude to B-flat Major for easier performance on the flute.

Polonaise

Transcribed by Louis Moyse

Carl Czerny
(1791–1857)

Sarabande
from *Pour le piano*

Transcribed by Louis Moyse

Claude Debussy
(1862–1918)

Spring Dance
(Springtanz)
from *New Lyric Pieces* (*Neue lyrische Stückchen*)

Transcribed by Louis Moyse

Edvard Grieg
(1843–1907)

12

Bourrée
from *Solos for a German Flute, a Hoboy or Violin*
No. 5 in G Major

Transcribed by Louis Moyse

George Frideric Handel
(1685–1759)

Little Dance

Transcribed by Louis Moyse

Franz Joseph Haydn
(1732–1809)

Venetian Gondolier
(Venetianisches Gondellied)
from *Songs Without Words (Lieder ohne Worte)*
Op. 30, No. 6

Transcribed by Louis Moyse

Felix Mendelssohn
(1809–1847)

Sarabande

Louis Moyse
(1912–2007)

Tempo di menueto

Allegro
second movement from Quartet in C Major
for Flute, Violin, Viola, and Violoncello, K. 285b

Transcribed by Louis Moyse

Wolfgang Amadeus Mozart
(1756–1791)

Allegretto
second movement from Fantasia in D minor, K. 397

Transcribed by Louis Moyse

Wolfgang Amadeus Mozart
(1756–1791)

Menuet in G Major
from *Clavierbüchlein II for Anna Magdalena Bach*
BWV Appendix 114

Transcribed by Louis Moyse

Christian Petzold
(1677–1733)

Premier Tambourin

fifth movement from *Pièces de clavecin en concert:*
Troisième concert, for harpsichord, violin (or flute) and viola da gamba (or second violin)

Transcribed by Louis Moyse

Jean-Philippe Rameau
(1683–1764)

Two Ecossaises
D. 299 and D. 977

Transcribed by Louis Moyse

Franz Schubert
(1797–1828)

The Merry Farmer, Returning from Work

(Fröhlicher Landmann, von der Arbeit zurückkehrend)

from *Album for the Young (Album für die Jugend)*, Op. 68, No. 10

Transcribed by Louis Moyse

Robert Schumann
(1810–1856)

Allegro
from Trio for Flute, Violin, and Continuo

Transcribed by Louis Moyse

Georg Philipp Telemann
(1681–1767)

Andante

Transcribed by Louis Moyse

Antonio Vivaldi
(1678–1741)